FOLENS
IDEAS BAN...
RE
BUDDHISM

C000079679

Lesley Prior

Contents

Folens
Publishers

How to use this book

Ideas Bank books provide ready to use, practical, photocopiable activity pages for children, **plus** a wealth of ideas for extension and development.

TEACHER IDEAS PAGE **PHOTOCOPIABLE ACTIVITY PAGE**

Clear focus to the activity.

Detailed background information to reinforce the topic.

Suggestions on how the children should approach the activities.

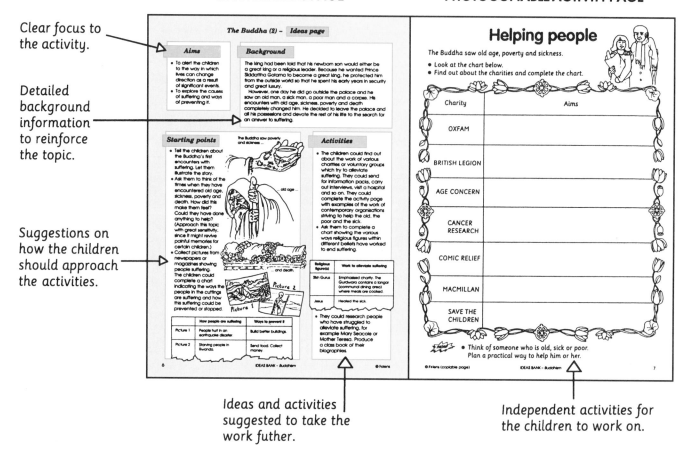

Ideas and activities suggested to take the work futher.

Independent activities for the children to work on.

- Time-saving, relevant and practical, **Ideas Bank** books ensure that you will always have work ready to hand.

Editor: Alyson Jones
Illustrations: Dandi Palmer

Layout artist: Patricia Hollingsworth
Cover image: Tony Stone Worldwide

© 1995 Folens Limited, on behalf of the author.

Every effort has been made to contact copyright holders of material used in this book. If any have been overlooked, we will be pleased to make any necessary arrangements.

First published 1995 by Folens Limited, Dunstable and Dublin.
Folens Limited, Albert House, Apex Business Centre, Boscombe Road, Dunstable, LU5 4RL, England.

ISBN 1 85276859-2

Printed in Singapore by Craft Print.

Introduction

This book sets out to enable children to learn about and from Buddhist insights, beliefs and practices. Clear explanation of the main features of the faith is provided, alongside relevant and feasible classroom activities. The book covers the needs of teachers and children from any religious background or none.

The structure of People, Beliefs, Special Places, Writings, Special Times and Festivals, which reflects most agreed syllabuses, should aid teachers' planning. Different faiths have different emphasis for these aspects. In the past, Buddhism has often been viewed as a deeply complex and philosophical religion, more suitable for sixth-form study than as a basis for activities for younger children. However, Buddhism is highly suitable as a focus for primary school RE as it offers an extremely practical approach to life and emphasises learning through experience.

The topics were selected with reference to SCAA Model Syllabuses and a range of LEA produced syllabuses and in full consultation with members of the relevant faith community. It is important to represent religions accurately and in a way that avoids inadvertently giving offence to members of the faith and also to develop positive and respectful attitudes in the children.

Teachers should avoid stereotyping, noting that there are certain beliefs and practices common to all Buddhists, but also variations in custom and practice. They should try to present what may be, to some children, unusual practices in a way that develops understanding and empathy, rather than mere curiosity.

The book is designed to provide interesting classroom activities together with background information for the teacher and suggestions for extension activities. Each activity is accompanied by sufficient information to enable the teacher to implement it without the need for further published material. It may be enriched by following the extension ideas on the Teachers' page and arranging visits, visitors and help from members of local faith communities, especially those already connected with the school.

The activity pages are designed to be used in various ways, as noted on the Ideas pages. They may be used to introduce a topic, drawing on the children's own experience or to continue exploration of a particular aspect of Buddhism. They may also be used for recording findings or ideas.

A glossary of useful terms is provided at the back of the book (page 48). This could be photocopied and used by the children to extend their vocabulary on Buddhism.

Useful Addresses:

The Buddhist Society
58 Eccleston Square
London SW1V 1PH

Tel: 0171 834 5858

(A directory of all Buddhist organisations in Great Britain can be provided from here.)

Articles of Faith Ltd
Resource House
Kay Street
Bury BL9 6BU

Tel: 0161 763 6232

(A set of Theravada Buddhist robes can be purchased from here.)

The Buddha (1) – Ideas page

The lotus flower is thought to be special because it is something beautiful that grows in dirty water.

Aims

- To learn about the birth of the Buddha.
- To explore some of the ways in which the Buddha's birth and the births of other famous people are shown to be important.

A white elephant appeared in a dream to the Buddha's mother.

Background

Prince Siddattha Gotama, the man who would become known to the world as the Buddha, was born in Lumbini, Nepal about 2500 years ago.

Before his birth, his mother had a strange dream in which a huge white elephant came into the room carrying a lotus flower. This indicated that the child she would bear would be both unusual and important.

This was reinforced by further signs when the child was eventually born – he was much larger than normal, he was already able to walk and lotus flowers sprung up wherever he stepped. There were special marks on his body and a wise man predicted that he would become a Buddha or 'Enlightened One'.

Starting points

- Ask the children to find pictures of famous people, for example sporting personalities, pop stars, actors, actresses, writers and members of the royal family. Discuss why these people are famous.
- They could sort their pictures into two piles (or complete a chart) indicating those people who have become famous and those who were famous from birth.
- In groups, select one person who has been famous since birth and investigate how the event was marked. For example, the birth of Prince William was celebrated with commemorative china and extensive press coverage. Display the results in a classroom interest area.

Famous people	Famous from birth	Famous for
The Beatles	No	Singing.
Louise Brown	Yes	First test-tube baby.
Prince Charles	Yes	Future king.

Activities

- Read the story of the events surrounding the birth of the Buddha. The activity page gives the children the opportunity to include the details of this story in an imaginary newspaper report.
- Ask the children to draw pictures and create a classroom wall display which re-tells the story of the Buddha's birth.
- Help the children to set up investigations into the birth stories of the founders of other religions, for example Jesus or Guru Nanak. What do they notice? They could record their findings in a chart such as the one below.

	Jesus	Buddha
Birthplace	Stable – very poor.	Palace – very rich.
Birthright	Son of a carpenter.	Son of a king.
Signs to show the child was special	Star over stable where born. Visited by three kings.	Able to walk when born. Lotus flowers sprung wherever he stepped.

The Buddha's birth

- Pretend you are a reporter for THE LUMBINI NEWS covering the story of the Buddha's birth.
- Write a report including a headline and picture.

THE LUMBINI NEWS

- Find out which famous people were born on your birthday. Were these people famous since birth or did they become famous?

The Buddha (2) – Ideas page

Aims

- To alert the children to the way in which lives can change direction as a result of significant events.
- To explore the causes of suffering and ways of preventing it.

Background

The king had been told that his newborn son would either be a great king or a religious leader. Because he wanted Prince Siddattha Gotama to become a great king, he protected him from the outside world so that he spent his early years in security and great luxury.

However, one day he did go outside the palace and he saw an old man, a sick man, a poor man and a corpse. His encounters with old age, sickness, poverty and death completely changed him. He decided to leave the palace and all his possessions and devote the rest of his life to the search for an answer to suffering.

Starting points

- Tell the children about the Buddha's first encounters with suffering. Let them illustrate the story.
- Ask them to think of the times when they have encountered old age, sickness, poverty and death. How did this make them feel? Could they have done anything to help? (Approach this topic with great sensitivity, since it might revive painful memories for certain children.)
- Collect pictures from newspapers or magazines showing people suffering. The children could complete a chart indicating the ways the people in the cuttings are suffering and how this suffering could be prevented or stopped.

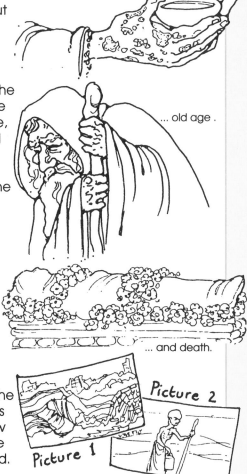

The Buddha saw poverty and sickness ...

... old age .

... and death.

Picture 2

Picture 1

	How people are suffering	Ways to prevent it
Picture 1	People hurt in an earthquake disaster.	Build better buildings.
Picture 2	Starving people in Rwanda.	Send food. Collect money.

Activities

- The children could find out about the work of various charities or voluntary groups which try to alleviate suffering. They could send for information packs, carry out interviews, visit a hospital and so on. They could complete the activity page with examples of the work of contemporary organisations striving to help the old, the poor and the sick.
- Ask them to complete a chart showing the various ways religious figures within different beliefs have worked to end suffering.

Religious figure(s)	Work to alleviate suffering
Sikh Gurus	Emphasised charity. The Gurdwara contains a langar (communal dining area) where meals are cooked.
Jesus	Healed the sick.

- They could research people who have struggled to alleviate suffering, for example Mary Seacole or Mother Teresa. Produce a class book of their biographies.

Helping people

The Buddha saw old age, poverty and sickness.

- Look at the chart below.
- Find out about the charities and complete the chart.

Charity	Aims
OXFAM	
BRITISH LEGION	
AGE CONCERN	
CANCER RESEARCH	
COMIC RELIEF	
MACMILLAN	
SAVE THE CHILDREN	

- *Think of someone who is old, sick or poor. Plan a practical way to help him or her.*

The Buddha (3) – Ideas page

The Buddha meditating in the lotus position under a Bodhi tree.

Aims

- To enable the children to explore various images of the Buddha.
- To begin to understand the use of symbolism in Buddhist art.

Starting points

- Read the story of the Buddha and find a picture of him to show the children. Why do they think the Buddha is often called the 'Enlightened One'? They could write down other questions and comments about the picture.
- Ask them to adopt the lotus position. Does this help them to relax and think? Why did the Buddha adopt this position under the Bodhi tree?
- Explore the way in which various facial expressions, hand gestures and body postures convey meaning. This could be done in a drama session or the children could draw illustrations.

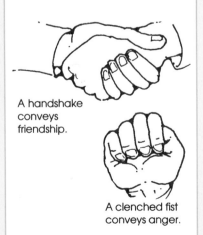

A handshake conveys friendship.

A clenched fist conveys anger.

Background

The Buddha travelled all over India in search of an answer to suffering. One day he sat thinking under a Bodhi tree. He adopted what we call the lotus position in order to help him relax and concentrate on meditating over the problem of suffering. Eventually he knew the answer (The Four Noble Truths) and spent the rest of his life teaching people that they too could find 'enlightenment'.

The Buddha is not worshipped, but revered by Buddhists and honoured for sharing his wisdom and teachings with them. Images of the Buddha (Buddharupas) are found in homes and places of worship and feature particular characteristics.

The hand gestures are symbolic, each conveying a different meaning. The mark between his eyebrows is sometimes called the 'eye of wisdom'. The bump of hair signifies both wisdom and the crown he abandoned. His long ear lobes recall the heavy earrings and wealth he gave up. His greatness is often represented by a halo and the use of gold paint (a precious metal) on the image.

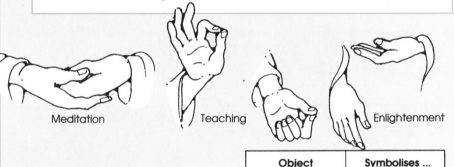

Meditation   Teaching   Enlightenment

Object	Symbolises ...
Halo	Holiness
Third eye	Enlightenment
Facial expression	Calmness
Simple clothes	Rejection of wealth

Activities

- Display models or pictures of the Buddha. The children could make a chart of the symbols they can see and what they represent. They could draw one or more of the images, noting as much detail as possible. Have they included any of the symbols they have noted on the chart?
- They could collect pictures showing portraits of various people, including religious leaders. Ask them to discuss the images and the symbols used. For instance, what other religions use halos as a symbol in their art?
- Ask them to use the activity page to create a symbolic portrait of a relative or friend. Encourage them to think about how facial expressions, posture, clothing, artefacts and so on can convey meaning and give information about the person.

Images and symbols

- Look at this picture of the Buddha.
- What can you see that shows:
  a) that he is wise?

  _____

  b) that he gave up his crown?

  _____

  c) that he gave up his wealth?

  _____

  d) that he is very special?

  _____

- Draw a picture of a relative or friend.
  Think of ways to show what sort of person he or she is.
  What symbols will you use?

The sangha (1) –   Ideas page

Aim

- To explore the concept of community in the Buddhist tradition and beyond.

Background

The word sangha means 'assembly' or 'community' and is used to refer to the entire Buddhist community, including lay people. However, it is generally taken to mean a religious community of monks or nuns. This consists of a group of individuals who have vowed to live their lives according to the teachings of the Buddha, abandoning the world and relying on the generosity of others to supply their needs.

The original Bhikkhus (monks) were homeless wanderers. Nowadays they can be found in the monasteries (viharas). Buddhist nuns are called Bhikkhuni.

All Buddhist monks and nuns can be identified by their shaved heads, robes and lack of possessions.

Starting points

- Explain the meaning of the word 'sangha'. Ask the children to compile a list of groups or clubs that they belong to, such as the Scouts, a youth club or a fan club.
- In groups the children could research a particular club or society. What brings the people who join together? What is the purpose of the group? How do the members express their unity?
- How would they identify a Buddhist monk or nun? Discuss the use of clothing to identify people in different groups. Do any of the groups and clubs they have looked at use dress to identify their members?

I joined the sangha:

1. To learn more about the teachings of the Buddha
2. To teach others about the life and work of the Buddha
3. To follow the Eightfold Path as fully as possible
4. To ensure a good re-birth and attain enlightenment
5. To meditate

Activities

- Contact the Buddhist Society (see page 3) to locate your nearest sangha. Ask the children to interview a monk or nun (in person or by letter) about the reasons why he or she joined the community. How do they express their beliefs through daily life?
- Using the activity page, ask the children to consider if the reasons to join a sangha and the reasons people join the clubs in the chart are similar in any way.

Group	Reason for joining
Sunday School	To learn more about God.
Girl Guides	To learn some skills and be with friends.
Football Team	To play better football and be with friends.

- They could investigate other groups or communities that have come together on account of religious beliefs. Where do they meet or live? What do they do? Are they easily identified? How?

Girl Guides

Sikhs

Salvation Army

Joining a club

- Find out why somebody might want to join the sangha.
- List some of the reasons below.

I joined the sangha:

- Find out why some people join different groups. Is it to help other people?
- Add some more examples of groups and complete the chart below.

Group	Reason for joining
Sunday School	
Girl Guides	
Football Team	

- Are any of the reasons people join similar?
  Why do you think this is?

The sangha (2) – Ideas page

Aims

- To encourage the children to explore their own daily lives.
- To learn about the daily life of a Buddhist monk or nun.

Background

Buddhist monks and nuns renounce worldly things. They are allowed to have only a few possessions – including two robes, sandals, an alms bowl for gifts of food and razor blades for shaving their heads.

They spend most of their time in meditation, reading sacred scriptures and learning more about the teachings of the Buddha. They share these teachings with others and in return, lay Buddhists give them food and other essentials. They eat only one meal a day which must be over by midday.

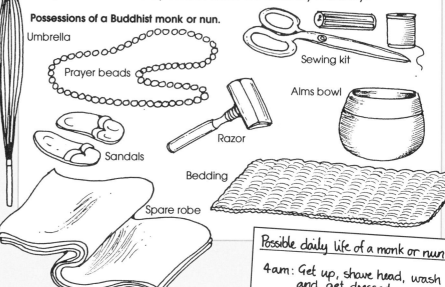

Possessions of a Buddhist monk or nun.

Umbrella
Prayer beads
Sandals
Razor
Bedding
Spare robe
Sewing kit
Alms bowl

Starting points

- Ask the children to list the things they use every day. For instance, a bed to sleep on, a car or bus to take them to school and so on. Are these things essential?
- What did the Buddha think about possessions (page 6)?
- Give the children a list of the possessions of a Buddhist monk. Why do they think the Buddhist monks need these things? What are they used for? How do the monks get these things?

Item	Used for
Razor	Shaving head.
Alms bowl	Collecting gifts.

- Ask the children to draw or list their favourite possessions or those things they think they cannot live without. What sort of things does a Buddhist monk live without? Discuss the differences.

Activities

- Discuss with the children the different aspects of their daily lives, including what they do, where they go, what they eat and so on. They could keep a diary, paying particular attention to the food they eat and the clothes they wear.
- Describe the daily life of a Buddhist monk or nun. Stress that this may vary according to each different tradition of Buddhism, but that all spend time meditating, receiving alms and reading the scriptures. Ask the children to write an imaginary diary entry for a Buddhist monk. They could complete the time chart on the activity page showing a day in the life of a monk or nun.
- Take the children to visit a sangha community to learn more about daily life there or write to one. Addresses can be obtained from the Buddhist Society (page 3).
- Invite the children to prepare a wall display showing a monk or nun with the only possessions he or she is allowed to have.

Possible daily life of a monk or nun

4 am: Get up, shave head, wash and get dressed
5 am: Chant with other monks or nuns
6 am: Meditation
11 am: Eat lunch (it must be eaten before midday)
12.30 pm: Domestic chores
2 pm: Alms round. (In the UK lay people would bring groceries to the vihara)
4 pm: Teaching
6 pm: Meditation
9 pm: Bed

The daily life of a monk or nun

- Below are some of the daily tasks of a monk or nun.
- Draw pictures in the blank boxes.

Dressing	Meditating	Eating
On the alms round	Teaching	Sleeping

 Every monk and nun spends some time each day in silent meditation.
- Find a place where you can sit quietly for a few minutes and close your eyes.
- What thoughts and feelings do you experience?

Hand position for meditating.

IDEAS BANK – Buddhism

The Law of Impermanence –

Aims

- To explore the meaning of the Law of Impermanence for Buddhists.
- To encourage the children to be aware of changes and their effects, both within their own lives and beyond.

Background

Because of his experiences in the outside world, the Buddha's life changed. He left his life of wealth and began teaching. He taught that impermanence is one of the basic facts of existence. Nothing in the world is fixed or unchanging.

Individuals are also subject to change – we are not the same people that we were five years, five weeks, five hours or even five minutes ago! Everyone continually experiences physical, mental and emotional changes and lives in a constantly changing world. For the Buddhist, it is therefore impossible to find lasting security.

Items that reflect impermanence.

Starting points

- Ask the children to think of things that change every day around them, for instance clouds, the weather, night into day and so on. They could make a list of things that do not last.

Things that do not last	
Cars	Rust.
Pens	Run out of ink.
Clothes	Wear thin.

- What changes have taken place in their own lives? For example moving home, changing school or class, growing taller and so on. How did they feel about these changes?
- Set up a display area of changes that have taken place, for example, in individuals, in the school, in the local area, in technology, in styles of fashion, music, art or in the natural world. Include written accounts, pictures, photographs, artefacts, music and interviews.

Activities

- Read the story of when the Buddha's life changed (page 6). Ask the children to complete the activity page, showing what changes occurred in his life as a result of his experiences.
- Invite each child to select a particularly important change in his or her life and to present this in the form of before and after pictures. Did they think the change was for better or worse?

Growing up is a sign of change.

- The Buddha established a way of life which he believed would help to put an end to suffering and bring about positive changes. In groups or as a class, devise a project to bring about positive changes. This could involve supporting a charity, engaging in voluntary work, organising a school grounds litter patrol and so on.
- Buddhists try to spend time in quiet meditation on the Law of Impermanence. Invite the children to sit quietly on the floor in a circle around a lighted candle. After five minutes, ask them if the flame is the same as it was at the beginning of the exercise. What else has changed during that time, in individuals, the room and beyond?
- Make a wall display around a collage of a lighted candle, using pictures summarising the children's responses.

Change

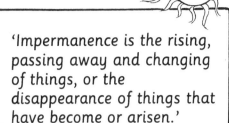

The Buddha taught that everything changes. His life changed from being a rich prince to a monk.

'Impermanence is the rising, passing away and changing of things, or the disappearance of things that have become or arisen.'

- Complete the timeline below to show what changes the Buddha made in his life.

The Buddha left the palace and saw old age.

He saw illness.

He saw the holy man who was very thin and never slept because he sat thinking all day .

- Make a timeline of your own life, showing any important changes that have taken place.

The Four Noble Truths – Ideas page

Aims

- To explore the meaning of the Four Noble Truths for Buddhists.
- To encourage the children to be aware of suffering, both within their own experience and beyond.
- To help them to develop suitable responses to suffering.

Background

After the Buddha realised the existence of suffering when he saw old age, sickness, poverty and death for the first time, his perception of the world was dramatically altered. He wanted to find an answer to this suffering.

While sitting meditating under a Bodhi tree, he thought of a suitable solution which is known as the Four Noble Truths and that is now at the centre of Buddhist teaching. The Four Noble Truths are:

1. Suffering exists.
2. Suffering is due to selfish desires.
3. The end of desire is the end of suffering.
4. The way to end suffering is through the Eightfold Path (see page 18).

Starting points

- Ask the children to think of times when they have felt unhappy or experienced suffering of some kind. They can either talk about this or write or draw pictures. Approach this activity with great sensitivity and be aware of any particularly difficult circumstances for individual pupils.
- Discuss the Four Noble Truths with the children. Ask them to discuss with a partner or in groups what they mean. Do they think that obeying these truths will help to prevent suffering? Why?
- Invite the pupils to produce collages for a classroom wall display which show their own perceptions of suffering. They could include pictures from newspapers and magazines and their own pictures and words.

My best friend moved away

My dad was ill

My uncle died

Ways to end suffering

Famine	Collect money by organising sponsored events, like a fun run or sponsored silence. Write to Parliament.
Illness	Collect money to send medical aid.

Activities

- Invite the children to engage in a survey of media reports, both in local and national newspapers and on the television, which focus on the suffering of individuals or communities. The results of the survey could be presented as a wall chart or as a class journal with daily entries.
- Ask the children to complete the activity page. Can they think of any other examples of suffering? Explore ideas such as racism and loneliness.
- They could investigate ways in which Buddhists work to alleviate suffering, by interviewing a local Buddhist or contacting various Buddhist organisations through the Buddhist Society (page 3).

The Four Noble Truths

The Buddha saw suffering and wanted to end it.

- Read the examples of suffering below. Illustrate them in the boxes. One has been done for you.

Famine   Illness   Poverty   War   Homelessness

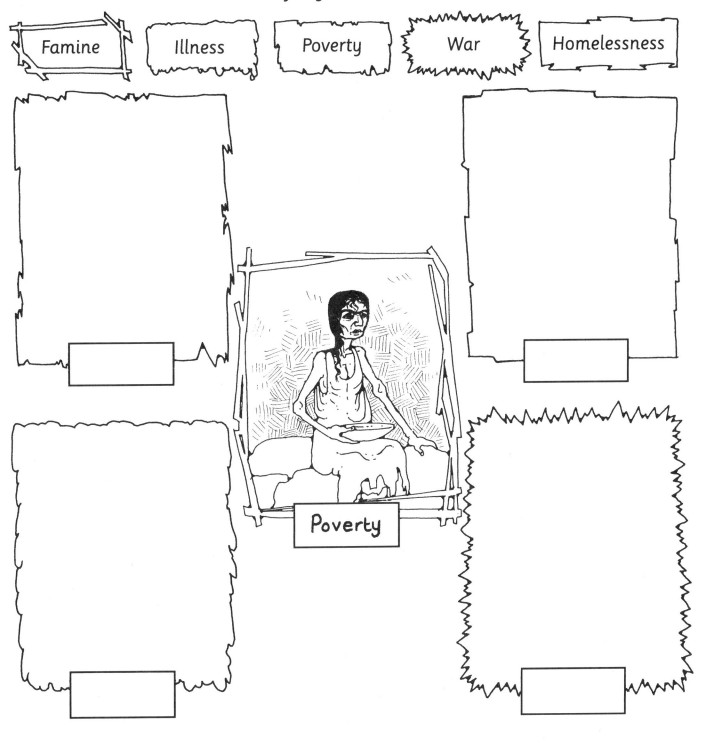

Poverty

- Why do you think these kinds of suffering exist?
  Can you think of ways to end them? Write a list overleaf.

The Eightfold Path – 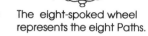 Ideas page

The eight-spoked wheel represents the eight Paths.

Aims

- To explore the meaning of the Eightfold Path for Buddhists.
- To encourage the children to understand the importance of rules both in a personal and wider context.

Background

The Eightfold Path is part of the basic Buddhist teaching (Dhamma). It was outlined by the Buddha himself when he delivered his first sermon. It is the means by which he believed suffering may be overcome and has provided his followers with a code of practice for living.

In Buddhist art, the dharmachakra (wheel of law) is often shown with eight spokes to symbolise the Eightfold Path.

The eight Paths are:
1. **Right Seeing** – the truth of the Four Noble Truths must be understood and accepted.
2. **Right Thought** – thoughts must be pure and unsullied by selfishness or unkindness.
3. **Right Speech** – there must be no idle gossip, lying or talking in any way which might encourage hatred or conflict.
4. **Right Action** – there should be no stealing, sexual misconduct or acting in any way which may harm or distress others.
5. **Right Livelihood** – this means adopting a way of life (including a job) which will be compatible with the Path.
6. **Right Effort** – a sincere effort must be made to live life in this way.
7. **Right Mindfulness** – being fully aware of the activities of the body, voice and also mind.
8. **Right Contemplation** – involves training the self in reflection and meditation.

Starting points

- Introduce the Eightfold Path and discuss its relevance for Buddhists. Ask a local Buddhist to talk to the children about its meaning for him or her.
- Discuss the school rules with the children and encourage them to think about the reasons for them. Ask them to illustrate the rules for a display in the school entrance area.
- Invite the children to discuss, collect and display as many sets of rules as possible, for example, The Highway Code, The Country Code, The Green Cross Code, The Firework Code, rules for various sporting activities and so on.

The religions represented by the symbols on page 19 are:

Sikhism

Hinduism

Christianity

Islam

Judaism

Activities

- Ask the children to complete the activity page. Can they think of any other symbols used in different religions?
- Invite the children to investigate the laws and rules to be found within other belief systems, for example The Ten Commandments, The Five Pillars of Islam, The Humanist Golden Rule and so on. What do they notice?
- Ask the children to develop their own sets of eight rules for home, school, class life and so on, either individually or in small groups. They could explain the reasons for their choices and present their rules to others using art materials, photographs or video film.
- Rules are often expressed as negatives, for example, 'Do not drop litter in the playground'. Challenge the children to collect some negative rules and then re-phrase them in a positive way. For example, 'Please help to keep the playground clean and safe for everyone' rather than 'No litter'. These can then be produced as new notices to be displayed in appropriate locations.

The Eightfold Path

The Eightfold Path provides Buddhists with a code of practice for living.

• What does the Eightfold Path say about the actions in each picture?

The Eightfold Path says _____

_____

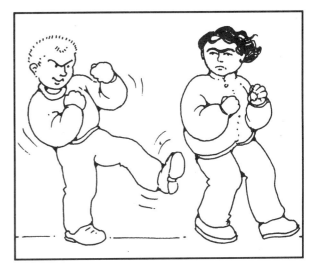

The Eightfold Path says ` _____

_____

The Eightfold Path says _____

_____

The Eightfold Path says _____

_____

 • The eight-spoked wheel is a symbol of Buddhism.
Which religions are represented by the symbols below?

The Middle Way – Ideas page

Aims

- To understand the concept of the Middle Way for Buddhists.
- To encourage the children to explore the importance of moderation, both within their own lives and beyond.

Starting points

- Ask the children to think of examples of how they practise moderation in their own lives and to give reasons. For example, eating sweets every day is bad for your teeth, going to bed late every night causes tiredness and so on.
- Ask each child or group of children to choose one example and design a poster (complete with slogan) which conveys the advantages of moderation. These could be displayed in appropriate locations around the school.

Background

The Buddha as a holy man of the forest.

The Buddha began his life in the privileged surroundings of a royal palace. His every whim was granted and all his desires fulfilled. Later, when he left his home in search of an answer to suffering, he became an ascetic and practised the greatest austerities. Legend tells us that he became so thin, he could feel his backbone from the front!

The Buddha eventually realised that both ways of life were extreme and neither should be recommended. Instead, he advocated a more moderate lifestyle, which is known as the Middle Way.

Things to do in moderation	How
Eating sweets.	Eat occasionally.
Watching television.	Watch one hour a night.
Playing outside.	Only until 7pm.

Activities

- Read the story of how the Buddha experienced both untold riches and pleasure and extreme poverty and hardship. Make a class chart showing the disadvantages of each and the advantages of leading a balanced life.
- Collect images that depict the two extremes of luxury and poverty and display them in the classroom. They could use the completed activity pages to make a book and add it to the display.

Possible lifestyle of a Buddhist

A Buddhist might live in a modest semi-detatched house and might have one car. They might be a nurse, teacher or lawyer. They might eat a balanced vegetarian diet and be involved in charity work. Although busy they would still find time for peaceful reflection.

- Ask the children to present the imaginary lifestyle of a Buddhist who is trying to live in accordance with the ideal of the Middle Way. They could present this as a story, drama or role play.

The Middle Way

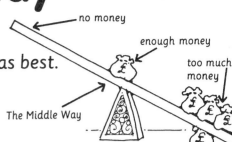

no money
enough money
too much money
The Middle Way

The Buddha was born very rich and then lived a very poor life. However he decided that the Middle Way was best.

- Look at the Buddha living the Middle Way below.
- Draw pictures of the different lifestyles of the Buddha before he decided to live that way.

	throne
	palace
	jewels
The Buddha as a rich prince.	plenty of food

	very thin
	wearing rags
The Buddha as a holy man of the forest.	no food

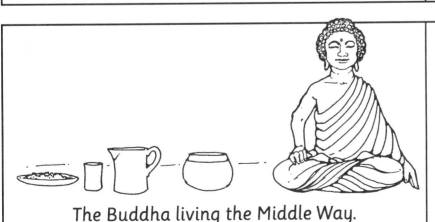

	some food
	clean, simple clothes
The Buddha living the Middle Way.	medium weight

- What are the differences? Add other words to the boxes.
- In groups, act out the life of the Buddha in three parts.

IDEAS BANK – *Buddhism*

The vihara – Ideas page

Aims

- To explore community life in the children's local area.
- To understand the role of the vihara within the Buddhist community.

A vihara can be in a residential house.

Starting points

- Explain the meaning of the word 'vihara'. Ask the children to suggest any places where they feel peaceful and thoughtful, for instance, a corner of the school grounds, a park, by the seashore and so on. Play some peaceful music while they write or draw the places they have mentioned.
- Ask the children to find out how their school serves the local community. Is it used by a play group, an after school care scheme or local interest societies?
- They could put this information into the school computer and print the results in the form of a brochure about the school. This could be available to visitors in the school entrance area.

Background

The word 'vihara' means 'abode' and is generally used to refer to a Buddhist temple which is also the home of a community of monks and nuns. In Britain these buildings vary in size and style. Some are sited in residential houses, while others are in purpose-built structures.

The vihara usually includes a shrine room, perhaps a meditation room, teaching facilities, a library and living quarters for the sangha. It provides a focus for the activities of the lay Buddhist community and is used for worship, meditation, rituals, festivals and as a centre for learning.

Shoes must be removed when entering the vihara.

The soles of the feet must not face towards the image of the Buddha.

A shop within the vihara will sell pamphlets, greeting cards and artefacts and there is usually an office where activities are co-ordinated.

Activities

- Try and arrange a visit to a vihara. The children could find out about the role of the vihara in Buddhist community life.
- They could contact the local library about buildings used by the community. What services are provided, such as sports facilities? Where do art and craft clubs or slimming groups meet? Design and produce a 'Community News' magazine for people who are new to the area.
- Ask the children to use the activity page to imagine they are a firm of architects with a commission to design a new vihara for a local Buddhist community. They must take into account the needs of the monks or nuns and the lay people.

The vihara

A vihara

- Imagine you are an architect. A local Buddhist community has asked you to design a new vihara.
- Draw your design below. Make sure you include all the things in the box on the right.

Images of the Buddha in the shrine room

Candles

Stupa

Library

Living quarters

Shoe rack

Flowers

Kitchen

The shrine room is the most important part of any vihara.
- Design a 'thinking corner' for your class or school. What sort of things would you put in it?

Pilgrimage sites – Ideas page

Aims

- To understand the importance of pilgrimage in the Buddhist tradition.
- To explore why certain places are important to members of the Buddhist community.

Starting points

- Ask the children to think of places they have visited and choose which is their favourite and give reasons. They could make a display in the classroom interest area of photographs, guidebooks and other souvenirs of their visits.
- What place would they like to visit if they could and why? Invite them to write down a list of reasons about their choice and make these into a class book.
- Create a word bank of adjectives that would describe the children's feelings if they visited their chosen place. Use examples such as a football supporter going to watch a home match, or a ballet lover's trip to their first show, to encourage ideas.
- Make a chart showing the most popular places visited by members of the class.

Background

In Buddhist tradition there are four main pilgrimage sites which are all linked with the life of the Buddha. These are his birthplace in Lumbini, Nepal, the place of his enlightenment at Bodh Gaya, the site of his first sermon near Varanasi and the area in which he died, Kusinara in north India (although the exact location is under dispute).

The Buddha recommended that his followers should try to visit each of these four sites because these places are linked to him and the key events in his life. Visiting these places should deepen a Buddhist's spiritual awareness, bring religious teachings to life and foster links with other Buddhists.

A map showing three of the main pilgrimage sites for Buddhism.

Varanasi, site of the Buddha's first sermon.

Lumbini, Nepal, the Buddha's birthplace

INDIA

Bodh Gaya, the place of the Buddha's enlightenment

(The area in which the Buddha died is not indicated on the map since the exact location is under dispute.)

—SRI LANKA

Activities

- Invite the children to suggest why these pilgrimage sites are important to Buddhists. They could research the answers in the library.
- They could make a list of places that are significant because of the people who were born, lived or died there.

Person	Place
Shakespeare	Stratford-upon-Avon – where he was born.
Henry VIII	Hampton Court Palace – where he lived.

- The children could create a travel brochure advertising one of the pilgrimage sites on the activity page. They could also produce a pictorial guide book for Buddhists going on the pilgrimage, listing things they could do.
- They could investigate sites of religious pilgrimage for other faiths and research why these places are important.

Pilgrimage site	Why visited
Bethlehem	Where Jesus was born.
Lourdes	Where the Virgin Mary appeared to St Bernadette.
Makkah	Site of the Holy Ka'bah.
Varanasi	Site of the Buddha's first sermon.

Pilgrimage sites

- Choose one of the places of pilgrimage below and design a travel brochure to advertise it.
- Think why the place is important and how you would encourage people to visit it.

Lumbini, Nepal, the Buddha's birthplace.

Near Varanasi, the site of the Buddha's first sermon.

Bodh Gaya, the place of the Buddha's enlightenment.

- Draw a picture story that shows what a Buddhist might do on this special holiday and how she or he might feel.

The Buddhist home – Ideas page

Aims

- To encourage the children to explore their feelings about their own homes.
- To learn about life within a Buddhist home.

Background

Buddhists live in all kinds of homes (houses, bungalows and flats). Their homes are much like everyone else's, but some may choose to have a small shrine area within their home.

This is a quiet place where a Buddhist can be alone to focus on their religious beliefs and practise meditation. The shrine would include an image of the Buddha (a buddharupa – to show he is an important person), flowers (to show that even beautiful things die), candles (to indicate that everything changes), a Bodhi leaf (to remember the Buddha's enlightenment) and a stupa (as a reminder that death comes to everyone).

Starting points

- Ask the children to make a list, using words or pictures, of places where quiet and respectful behaviour is necessary, for example a library, a museum and a hospital. Invite them to explain the reasons for this type of behaviour.
- Ask the children to think about their homes. Invite them to draw or write about the most special part of their homes. How do they show it is special?
- Discuss where the children go when they want to be quiet or alone when they are at home. They could give reasons for their choice. Why are these quiet places like the Buddhist shrine area?

The puja area in my home is very special.

The shabbat table in my home is special.

I go to my bedroom to be quiet and alone. It has all my favourite things in it.

A Hindu puja tray

A Muslim prayer mat and prayer beads

Activities

- Invite the children to bring in objects which are particularly special to them and to explain the reasons for their choices. Encourage Jewish children to bring in items from the shabbat table and Hindu children could bring in items from the puja area in their homes. Display these items in a class interest area.
- Ask the children to complete the activity page on the shrine area in the Buddhist home. They could make or draw the objects shown and create their own Buddhist shrine area.
- They could research what religious artefacts could be found in the homes of people from other religious faiths. They could complete a chart.

A kippah

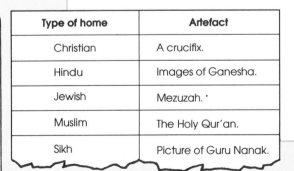

Type of home	Artefact
Christian	A crucifix.
Hindu	Images of Ganesha.
Jewish	Mezuzah.
Muslim	The Holy Qur'an.
Sikh	Picture of Guru Nanak.

A mezuzah

The Buddhist home

The objects below could be found in the shrine area in a Buddhist home. They all have a special meaning.

● Match the correct meaning to each object and write the name.

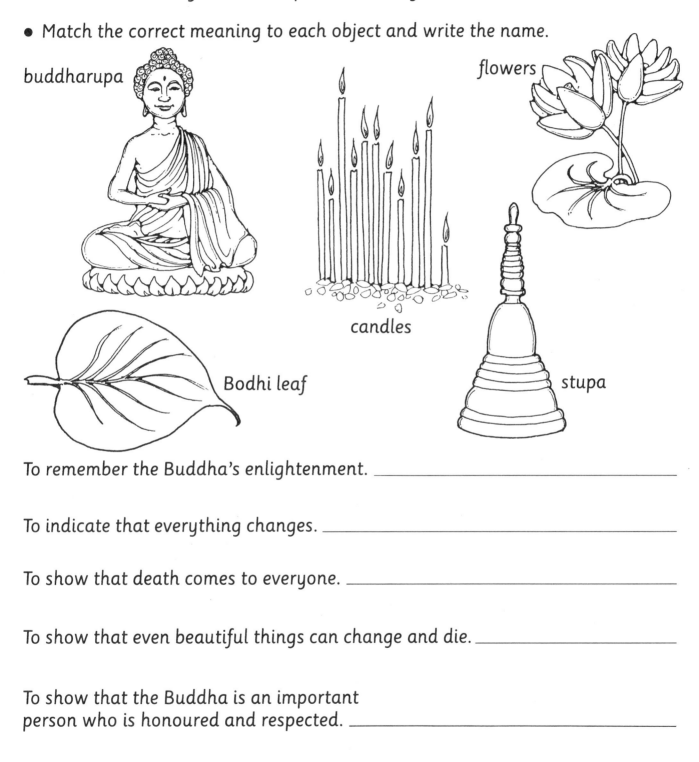

buddharupa

flowers

candles

Bodhi leaf

stupa

To remember the Buddha's enlightenment. _____

To indicate that everything changes. _____

To show that death comes to everyone. _____

To show that even beautiful things can change and die. _____

To show that the Buddha is an important
person who is honoured and respected. _____

 ● Think about how you show that someone is
special to you. Write a list of ways overleaf.

The Buddha and the wounded swan – Ideas page

Aims

- To explore the Buddhist perspective on animal rights issues.
- To encourage the children to develop their own moral viewpoints through engaging in debate with others.

Starting points

- Tell the story of the Buddha and the wounded swan.
- How does the story convey Buddhist attitudes towards living things? How do Buddhists express this in their daily lives?
- Ask the children to complete the activity page, suggesting what the prince and Devadatta might have said to argue their cases before the judge.
- Set up a class re-enactment of the scene using the best suggestions from the completed activity pages as part of the script.

Background

One day, Prince Siddattha was walking in the grounds of the beautiful palace where he lived. Suddenly a swan landed at his feet and to his horror, he saw that it was wounded. The young prince was distressed and tried to help the bird by gently pulling out the arrow that had injured its wing.

His cousin, Devadatta, had shot the swan while out hunting and claimed it for his own, but the prince refused to give him the creature he had harmed. Unable to resolve their dispute, the two cousins decided to consult a judge on the matter. Eventually, after much deliberation, he announced that it is better to give life than to take it and presented the bird to Siddattha who took the swan and when it had recovered, he set it free.

Buddhists should respect all living things. Many are vegetarians. These beliefs are also shared by members of other faith traditions. Jain monks, for example, wear small muslin masks over their mouths to prevent breathing in and swallowing tiny insects. They also brush the ground infront of them to prevent treading on any insects.

- I enjoy hunting
- Hunting is a tradition
- There are plenty of other swans
- Young men of my background are expected to hunt
- When I hunt, I am learning the skills to be a great warrior

- We should not be cruel to animals
- The swan had not hurt Devadatta
- The swan was not killed to be eaten
- The swan was only killed for sport or pleasure, which is cruel
- Swans are beautiful, gentle animals and should be protected

Devadatta   Prince Siddattha

Activities

- Conduct a survey to find out how many vegetarians there are in the school and their reasons for not eating meat. The children could write a menu for a vegetarian meal.

Pupil	Reason for not eating meat
Susan	I love animals.
Mark	I don't like the taste of meat.

- They could research and discuss other topics that link with animal rights issues, for example, animals in zoos and circuses, hunting, the fur trade and laboratory animals. They could produce wall charts summarising the main points of argument for and against within each debate.
- Encourage the children to debate one or more of these issues and elect speakers.

The Buddha and the wounded swan

Devadatta shot the swan while hunting and wanted to keep it.
Prince Siddattha refused to give him the creature he had harmed.
Unable to resolve their argument they went to see a judge.

- What do you think they might have said to the judge?
  Write down your suggestions in the speech bubbles.

Prince Siddattha

Devadatta

- Find out about the ways in which a Jain
  monk tries not to harm any living creature
  and write them overleaf.

A Jain monk

The Buddha and the angry elephant – Ideas page

Aims

- To encourage the children to explore the emotion of jealousy.
- To introduce a story from the Buddhist tradition that focuses on this theme.

Background

The Buddha spent many years travelling across India sharing his teachings with others. Among his followers was his cousin, Devadatta (see page 28) who was jealous of the Buddha and sought to harm him.

Devadatta even planned to kill the Buddha, but in such a way that his death would appear to be an accident. He took an elephant and encouraged the unfortunate creature to drink several buckets of rice wine. Soon the elephant was drunk and became wild and dangerous. It ran wildly at the Buddha and the crowd of people he was teaching, causing havoc as the frightened people ran away. Devadatta waited, confident that it would destroy his cousin, but the Buddha calmly stood in front of the distressed animal until it was quiet. Eventually, the elephant bowed before the great teacher and Devadatta knew that he had failed.

Starting points

- Read the story of the Buddha and the angry elephant. Have the children ever felt jealous and if so, why? Can they explain what made them jealous?
- Collect and read stories that illustrate jealousy and discuss these with the children. These could be factual or fictional and could come from a variety of religious traditions. Some examples include *Joseph and his Technicolour Dreamcoat* and *The Prodigal Son*.

She's got a better bike than me.

He's got a brother and I haven't.

She's got long hair and mine's short.

Activities

- Why do the children think Devadatta was jealous of the Buddha? They could make a list of reasons.
- They could complete the activity page and then write their own story about jealousy.
- They could act out the story of the Buddha and the angry elephant. They could produce short role plays or dramas about jealousy. These could be based on the stories they have heard or could be invented by the children.
- Ask the children to present an imaginary newspaper report and headline about the incident. They could write imaginary interviews with the Buddha, Devadatta, witnesses, an elephant keeper and perhaps a psychiatrist who could comment on why Devadatta wanted to harm his cousin.

The jealous witch gave Snow White a poisoned apple.

Cinderella was not allowed to go to the ball because the ugly sisters were jealous of her.

BUDDHA IN INCIDENT WITH ANGRY ELEPHANT

The Buddha and the angry elephant

- Cut out the pictures and put them in order to tell the story. You could add captions to the pictures.

- What do you think the Buddha might have said at the end of the story? How do you think Devadatta might have felt?
- Write your own story about jealousy and illustrate it.

Ananda – Ideas page

A glass stupa

Aim

- To explore how people are remembered after their deaths through the story of Ananda.

Starting points

- Discuss with the children how they remember people or animals that they have known but who are now dead. For example, through talking about them, by looking at photographs or visiting a grave. Great sensitivity will be needed during this session, particularly if there are children who have been recently bereaved.
- Ask the children to investigate how and why famous people are remembered. If possible they should focus on a person who lived or worked in your locality. They could make their work into a commemorative book.

Background

The Buddha spent many years as a holy man travelling about the country to share his teachings with others. The Sutta Pitaka is a collection of scriptures containing the main dialogues of the Buddha.

When he was about eighty years old, he died, leaving his followers lost and unhappy.

Ananda, a relative of the Buddha, had been particularly devoted to him and was devastated by his death. However, he was persuaded by a young monk to put his grief behind him and continue the work of his master for the sake of others.

A stupa (or memorial) is often erected over the remains of an important Buddhist who has died. These serve to remind Buddhists that, like the Buddha himself, everyone is mortal and will die one day. (Small glass stupas are often used to cover small images of the Buddha to remind people of this).

The truths taught by the Buddha will live on, especially while there are those who wish to continue his work as Ananda did.

Charles Darwin was born near our town.

He was a famous scientist.

There is a statue of him in the town centre.

There is a shopping precinct named after him.

Activities

Where many Buddhists can be found today

- Tell the story of Ananda. Invite the children to discuss how and why the grief-stricken young man decided to continue the Buddha's work. Other reasons might be that he thought the Buddha had been kind, that he had helped the poor, that he had been an important leader and that he had dedicated his life to others.
- The children could set up investigations into how and why the Buddha is remembered today. They could research the spread of Buddhism and show the results on a wall map. Are there any Buddhists in the local area?
- Challenge them to find out about stupas and design a memorial for the Buddha or person of their choice.

IDEAS BANK – *Buddhism*   © Folens

Ananda

- Think of more reasons why Ananda decided to continue the Buddha's work.
- Write them in the thought bubbles.

He greatly admired and respected the Buddha.

He helped the people to live their lives in the best way.

He tried to help the sick.

Ananda

 • Make a list of ten people who have had an important influence on you. Discuss the reasons for your choices with a partner.

Birth rituals – Ideas page

Aims

- To explore why some people like to celebrate the birth of a child.
- To learn how this may be expressed within the Buddhist community.

Background

There are no specific ceremonies in Buddhism to celebrate the birth of a child. However, one important Buddhist belief is to value and cherish all living things. New life is therefore cherished by Buddhists.

Some Buddhist parents may choose to mark the birth of a new child by inviting monks into their home to chant paritta (texts thought to give blessing and protection). In return, the parents may offer gifts to the monks.

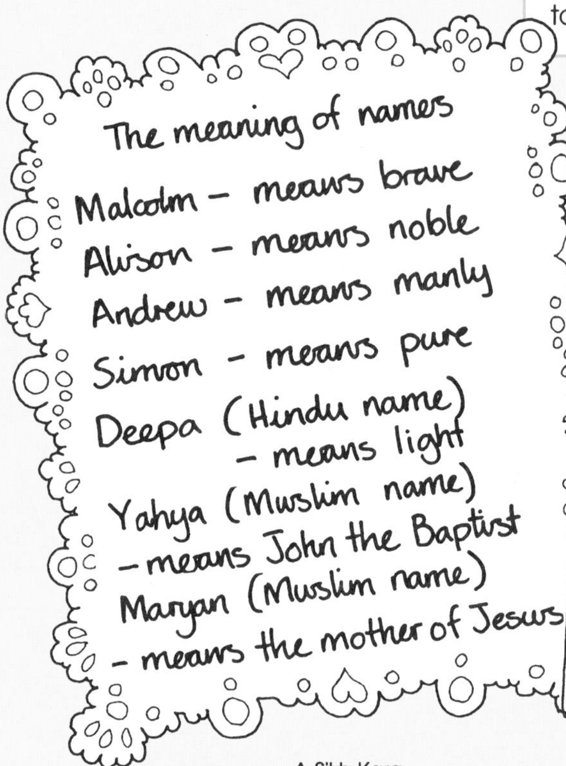

Starting points

- Help the children to discuss why the birth of a baby is usually welcomed and ways of marking the occasion. Invite them to collect and display announcements, greetings cards, celebratory balloons and so on.
- Ask the children to design and make their own baby books, recording when and where they were born, their birth weights and so on. Photographs and other artefacts could be included.
- They could investigate the meaning of names of children in the class. Do these names indicate what hopes the parents have for the children?

The meaning of names

Malcolm – means brave

Alison – means noble

Andrew – means manly

Simon – means pure

Deepa (Hindu name) – means light

Yahya (Muslim name) – means John the Baptist

Maryan (Muslim name) – means the mother of Jesus

Toys are a popular present for a baby.

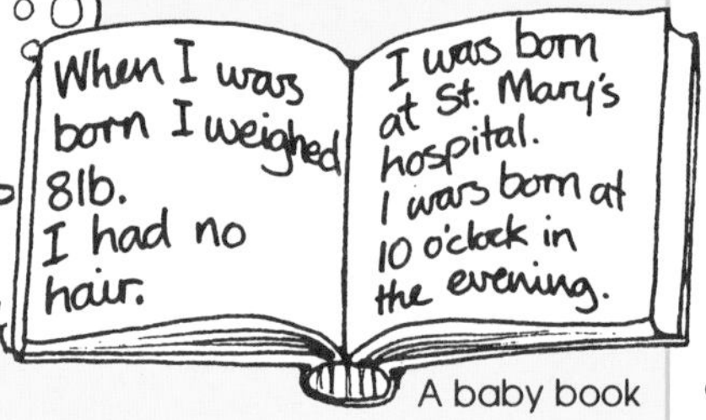

When I was born I weighed 8lb. I had no hair.

I was born at St. Mary's hospital. I was born at 10 o'clock in the evening.

A baby book

A Sikh Kara

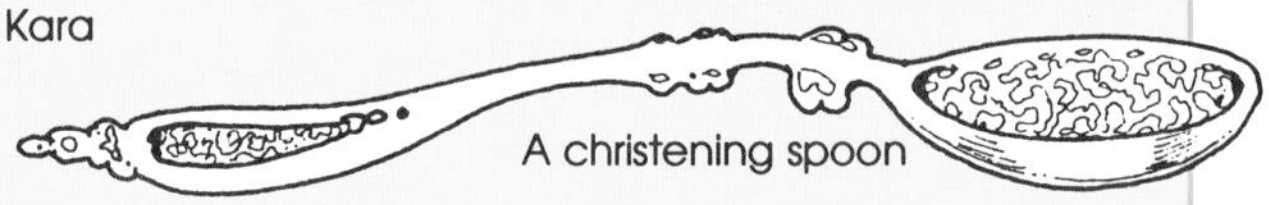

A christening spoon

Activities

- Encourage the children to find out what happens when a baby is born in a Buddhist family. Complete the activity page to suggest what Buddhists might hope for a newborn child.
- Help the class to research the birth rituals used within other faiths. They could complete a chart or produce a display using pictures, posters, books, video film and so on.
- Ask the children to design and make birth congratulations cards to send to parents from different faith traditions and to those without religious belief.

Faith	Birth rituals
Christianity	Baptism. The baby's head is covered with water. The parents are given a candle to hold during the ceremony.
Sikhism	The Guru Granth Sahib is opened at random and the first letter of the hymn that appears on the left-hand page becomes the first letter of the child's name.
Judaism	Brit Milah (circumcision) occurs when a male child is eight days old. When a baby girl is born, her father announces her name in the synagogue on the first Shabbat after her birth.

Birth rituals

In the story of Sleeping Beauty, the good fairies
wished her to be kind, gentle and happy.
Buddhist monks sometimes chant blessings when a baby is born.

The good fairies

- What do you think they might hope for a
  new baby? Complete the speech bubbles below.

- Find out what messages and presents you
  and your family received when you were born.

Ordination – Ideas page

Aims

- To explore how responsibilities increase as people grow older.
- To look at the particular significance of this within the Buddhist community.

Starting points

- Ask the children to create time lines of their lives and to comment on how things have changed since their early years.
- Invite them to research how old a person must be to vote, drive, stay at home alone, pay adult fares on the bus and so on. They could display the results with appropriate pictures.
- Ask them to list some of the responsibilities that come with adulthood and present them as a wall chart.

Responsibilities that may come with adulthood
1. The right to vote
2. Earning a living
3. Paying bills
4. Being independent
5. Being in a relationship
6. Having children

WATER DEMAND
ELECTRIC BILL

Background

As people grow older they take on new responsibilities and make difficult decisions. Leaving home is a sign of growing up and signifies having to give up childish things.

In some Buddhist countries there is an initiation ceremony for children approaching adolescence, although the age of the candidates does vary. He or she is admitted to the sangha as a novice monk or nun in a special ceremony. They stay in the monastery for varying lengths of time – a night, a few weeks or years or even forever.

The style of the ceremony varies according to the local custom. In some cases, the children are dressed as princes and princesses and parade with great splendour to the monastery. Here, in emulation of the Buddha, they abandon their 'royal' status and are dressed in simple robes and have their heads shaved. The time they spend in the sangha allows them to study the teachings of the Buddha and develop a greater understanding of them.

The children have their heads shaved before they enter the monastery.

Activities

Sandals

Robe

Umbrella

Alms bowl

Objects a child might be given when entering the monastery.

- Help the class to investigate the ceremonies that mark ordination into the Buddhist tradition. The children could write to the Buddhist Society (page 3) or interview a local Buddhist.
- They could complete the activity page and make a class word bank of words associated with how a Buddhist might feel at their ordination.
- Make a class book celebrating an imaginary ordination. Illustrate it with the children's pictures and drawings.
- Encourage the children to find out how other faith communities mark the transition to adulthood, for example, the Hindu Sacred Thread ceremony, the Sikh Amrit ceremony and so on.

Faith	Transition to adulthood
Roman Catholicism	Confirmation.
Judaism	Bar/Bat Mitzvah.
Sikhism	Amrit ceremony.

Ordination

Imagine you are leaving home to stay in a Buddhist monastery for a few weeks. Draw yourself in the space below.

- Draw a line from you to the possessions you will be given.
- Cross out those possessions you must give up.

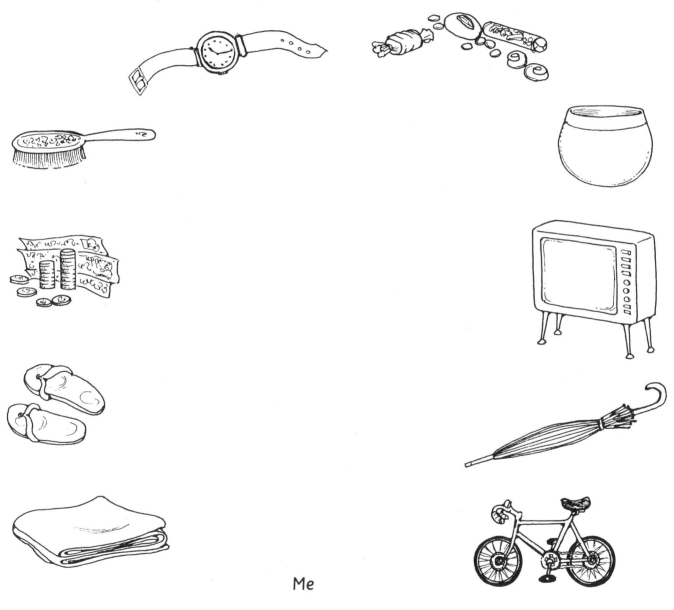

Me

- Write a story about how you might feel on this special day. Use some of the words below to help you.

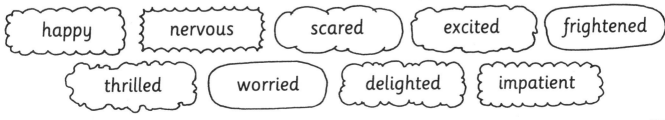

happy   nervous   scared   excited   frightened

thrilled   worried   delighted   impatient

Marriage – Ideas page

Aims

- To explore why some couples choose to affirm their commitment to one another in marriage.
- To learn about the ceremony of marriage within the Buddhist faith.

Background

There is no specific ceremony for marriage in the Buddhist tradition. Weddings are secular, but there may be an opportunity for monks to be involved in reciting from the paritta to give blessings and protection to the couple.

In some Buddhist cultures the union of a couple may be symbolised by a thread that binds together the thumbs of their right hands.

In the west, where marriage ceremonies are often religious, some attempts are now being made to draw up Buddhist wedding ceremonies that include appropriate prayers, blessings and readings. Often the bride and groom are led to a special platform that is decorated with white flowers.

The couple are married on a special platform decorated with flowers.

Starting points

- Discuss with the children the possible advantages and disadvantages of being married. Ask them to present the key issues in a class debate.
- Ask the children to suggest some promises that would be appropriate for a bride and groom to make as a sign of their commitment to one another. These suggestions could be made into a class book.
- Encourage them to collect and display material relating to weddings such as invitations, greetings cards and photographs.

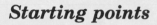

Garlands and ornate hand markings are popular at Hindu weddings.

Activities

- Ask the children to investigate marriage ceremonies within the Buddhist tradition. They could refer to books, videos, posters and so on. If possible they could interview a local Buddhist.
- Arrange a mock wedding for a Buddhist couple. The children could write the words that could be used and act the key roles.
- Invite the children to research other types of wedding ceremonies, both religious and secular. They could present their findings through a computerised database or on a chart. They could collect illustrations which show the differences between the ceremonies of different faiths.

Faith	Wedding ceremony
Christianity	The bride usually wears white. Rings are exchanged.
Judaism	The couple are married under a huppah (canopy) and share a goblet of wine which they drink and then smash.
Sikhism	The bride usually wears red and has ornate hand and face markings. The bride and groom are joined together with a scarf (chuni) to symbolise their union.

Jewish couples share a goblet of wine.

- Ask the children to create a multi-media wall display depicting the various items used to symbolise the union of a couple, such as threads, rings, scarfs and the huppah. They could devise a Buddhist wedding symbol for the invitation on the activity page.

Marriage

Imagine you are an artist and a Buddhist couple has asked you to design their wedding invitation.

- Use these symbols and emblems in your design.

- Draw your wedding invitation design in the space below.

- Write a poem to send to the couple on their wedding day.

Death and funerals – Ideas page

Aims

- To help the children to consider what might happen after death.
- To explore the Buddhist response to this question.

Starting points

- Read *I'll always love you* by Hans Wilhelm (Picture Knight) and discuss with the children how the boy felt when his dog died. Invite them to be aware of the mourning rituals described in the book.
- Read *Badger's parting gifts* by Susan Varley (Picture Puffin) or *The Mountains of Tibet* by Mordicai Gerstein (Barefoot Books). Discuss with the children different ideas about what happens after death.

- Ask the children to research and investigate the beliefs of different faith communities about death, including the Buddhist community. They should present their findings in a class forum or on a chart.

Background

When a Buddhist dies, he or she is cremated. Monks read from the scriptures and preach to the mourners, reminding everyone of the impermanence of life. After the cremation there may be other rituals designed to win merit for the deceased and these might include feeding the monks or presenting them with new robes.

Buddhists believe in a cycle of reincarnation until a state of perfect kamma or enlightenment has been reached. This enables the person to reach the deathless realm of nirvana. A person's state of mind immediately before death is therefore extremely important since this may determine the destination of the soul. Family, friends, and perhaps monks, will gather to recite scriptures and in Tibet there may be readings from the *Book of the Dead* which is a book that discusses the concept of reincarnation.

Remember to approach this topic with great care and sensitivity.

Activities

- Set up a class debate about organ donation after death with speakers both for and against. Do the children feel this is an appropriate way for someone to help others? Does it enable a person to carry on 'living' after death?
- Buddhists believe in reincarnation. Help the children to explore cycles in the natural world such as apples, frogs and rain. They could create a wall display of different life cycles.

The life cycle of a butterfly.

Faith	Funeral rites	Belief
Christianity	Bodies are cremated or sometimes buried.	Belief in an after-life.
Hinduism	Bodies are cremated.	Belief in reincarnation.
Islam	Bodies buried facing the Holy City of Makkah.	Belief in an after-life, but in Islam there is a strong concept of heaven and hell.
Sikhism	Bodies are cremated.	Death is viewed like falling asleep and the person wakes up into a new life.

Reincarnation

Buddhists believe in a cycle of reincarnation. This means that after death, a person is born again in another form.

- Complete the questionnaire below to help you decide what to come back as in your next life.

NEXT LIFE QUESTIONNAIRE

NAME _____

I want to be:
Human   Male ☐
            Female ☐

Animal   Cat ☐
          Dog ☐
          Bird ☐
          Tiger ☐
          Mouse ☐
          Spider ☐
          Other _____

an alien ☐

Other _____

I want to live on planet:
   Mars ☐
   Jupiter ☐
   Earth ☐   in Italy ☐
             India ☐
             Russia ☐
             Other _____

Other _____

I want to live in:
a castle ☐
a canal boat ☐
a sweetshop ☐
Other _____

I want to be:
strong ☐
kind ☐
clever ☐
Other _____

I want to be:
a spy ☐
a nurse ☐
a popstar ☐
Other _____

I want to be able to:
fly ☐
swim ☐
sing ☐
Other _____

 • Write a story about a day in your new life.

   IDEAS BANK – Buddhism

Wesak – Ideas page

Aim

- To encourage the children to explore the significance of celebration in their own lives.
- To look at the celebration of Wesak in the Buddhist community.

Background

Wesak (the festival of light) is the Sri Lankan word for the month of May. Buddhists believe that it was in that month that the most significant events of the Buddha's existence took place. His birth, enlightenment and death all happened in that month. Celebrations are usually held on the day of the first full moon in late May/early June.

Wesak is now celebrated in a variety of ways by Buddhists all over the world. In Sri Lanka the streets are decked with lanterns, in Thailand there are processions and candles are lit as symbols of hope and wisdom while in Japan, statues of the Buddha are washed with scented water.

Examples of material for the class interest area on celebrations.

Starting points

- Discuss different kinds of celebrations with the children and set up a class interest area with photographs, greetings cards, candles and special menus to reflect these celebrations.
- Create a class word bank of any words used to describe the feelings associated with special times and celebrations.

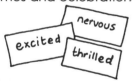

nervous
excited
thrilled

- Ask the children to write stories, individually or in groups, about one type of celebration, either religious or secular. Encourage them to use the word bank to focus on feelings associated with celebrations.

In Japan, statues of the Buddha are washed with scented water.

Activities

- Encourage the children to set up a corridor display to inform the rest of the school about Wesak, featuring pictures, posters and captions.
- The children could complete the activity page and then design a card celebrating Wesak. The most successful designs could be sent to local Buddhists.
- Wesak celebrates the life of the Buddha. Ask the children to investigate other religious festivals which are linked to key figures. For instance, Christian saint days and the Hindu festival of Divali which is based on the story of Rama and Sita. They could make a chart or collect pictures of the different festivals. Why do these celebrations take place and why are these people still remembered today?

Festival	Religion	Key figure(s)
Divali	Hinduism	Rama and Sita
Gurpurbs	Sikhism	The Gurus
Purim	Judaism	Esther
St Patrick's Day	Christianity	St Patrick

42

IDEAS BANK – Buddhism

© Folens

Wesak

Wesak is celebrated all over the world.

Wesak is celebrated on the day of the first full moon in late May.

- Circle the three reasons below why Buddhists celebrate Wesak.

to remind them of the Buddha's birth	to present robes to the monks	to remind them of the Buddha's enlightenment
to remind them of the Buddha's death	to give alms to the monks	to celebrate a new year

- Look at the three pictures below which show Buddhists celebrating in different countries. Complete the sentences.

In Sri Lanka, the streets are

decorated with _____ .

In Japan, statues of the

_____ are

washed with scented water.

In Thailand, there are

candles and _____ .

The candles are lit as symbols

of _____ and wisdom.

- Write a story about a Buddhist child in one of these countries celebrating Wesak.

Bodhi Day – | Ideas page

Aims

- To explore the symbolism of light.
- To consider the importance Buddhists attach to celebrating the enlightenment of the Buddha.

Background

Bodhi Day falls in the month of December and commemorates the time when the Buddha sat beneath a Bodhi tree and achieved enlightenment.

Many Buddhist shrines now feature a cutting from a descendant of the original tree as a reminder of this event and as an aid to meditation. The leaves are pointed and heart-shaped and are often used as a decorative and symbolic motif in Buddhist art.

Lights and lanterns feature in the Bodhi Day celebrations to show that when the Buddha became enlightened he passed from darkness into light and could clearly see the truth about life and suffering for the first time.

Leaf motif on a Buddhist temple in Thailand.

Starting points

- Ask the children to sit, in silence, in a circle on the floor. Darken the room as much as possible. After five minutes, light a candle and sit in silence for another five minutes. Encourage the children to discuss their responses to light and dark.
- Tell the story of the Buddha's enlightenment and discuss with the children how his teaching is a light for others to show them the way to live.
- Set up a display area on light. The children could brainstorm words connected with darkness and light and make them into a montage. They could bring in different lights, such as torches, bicycle lamps, lamps and Christmas tree lights. They could explain how and why each item is used.

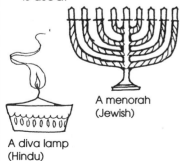
A diva lamp (Hindu)

A menorah (Jewish)

Activities

- Photocopy the activity page on to pale green paper before giving it to the children. The completed Bodhi leaf could then be cut out and mounted on a tree trunk display in the classroom.

- Ask the children to make a class book of biographies of people who have been a 'light' to others. These could be religious or secular figures or famous or not-so-famous people.
- What other religious festivals use light in their celebrations? The children could research what light represents at these different celebrations. For instance, at the Sikh Divali festival light symbolises the celebrations at the homecoming of Guru Har Gobind, often in Christian festivals light symbolises hope and so on.

Religion	Festival	Significance
Hinduism	Divali	Festival of lights.
Judaism	Hanukkah	Eight-day festival of light.
Christianity		

Bodhi Day

The Buddha was a 'light' in the world because he helped people.

- Think of a way that you could be a 'light' in the world.
- Write or draw your idea on the Bodhi leaf and cut it out.

The Buddha meditated under the Bodhi tree.

Cuttings from the Bodhi tree are found in some Buddhist shrines.

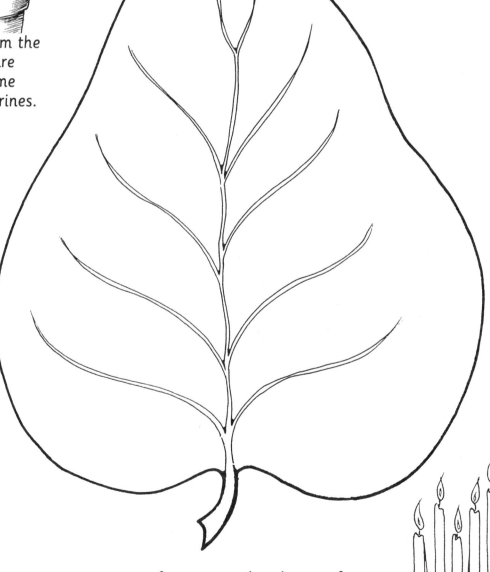

- Cut out a piece of paper in the shape of a candle. Write words on it that describe light.

Kathina Day – Ideas page

Aims

- To consider how clothes are linked to celebrations.
- To look at the celebration of Kathina Day within the Buddhist tradition.

Background

Traditionally, Buddhist monks travelled around the countryside sharing their wisdom with others. During the rainy season they would go into retreat and spend their time quietly in meditation. At the end of the retreat, lay people present the monks with gifts, including cloth for new robes.

This custom is still followed in some Buddhist countries, such as Thailand, but as there is no set rainy season in this country, the practice has been adapted to suit a different climate. Monks in this country still go into a retreat and receive cloth for new robes on Kathina Day which usually occurs in October and is marked with special ceremonies at the vihara.

The colour of their robes indicates which tradition each monk or nun belongs to. For instance, Tibetan Buddhists wear maroon, Theravadas wear saffron robes, Zen traditionalists wear black and trainee monks and nuns wear white.

Starting points

- Ask the children to draw or write about some of their clothes. What do they wear and why?
- They could collect pictures of different uniforms and make these into a class book. Ask them to add explanations of various features of each one.
- What clothes do people wear when it rains? What alternatives are there to going out on rainy days? What do Buddhist monks do?

The clothes people wear when it rains:

Waterproof coat
Umbrella
Wellington boots
Hat

Activities

- Help the children to gather information about Kathina Day and the life of Buddhist monks. They could create a wall display of a Buddhist monk or nun in their robes and with their possessions around them.
- Ask the children to complete the activity page. They should think about the colours used for robes in the three main strands of Buddhism and could use scraps of fabric to complete the robes.
- The children could research the lives and traditions of Christian monks, such as Benedictines or Carthusians and compare and contrast these with those in the Buddhist tradition. What differences do they notice about the clothes the monks wear?
- On a rainy day, encourage the children to sit in silence in the classroom and think of all the benefits of rainfall, instead of the fact that they cannot go out to play. Ask them to record their thoughts to share with others.

A Buddhist monk and a Christian monk.

The benefits of rainfall are:
It waters the crops, flowers and gardens. It fills the reservoirs. It fills ponds and provides water for wildlife.

Kathina Day

On Kathina Day, the lay people present the monks with gifts including material for a new robe. The monk below has made this material into a new robe for the celebration.

- Choose which tradition your monk belongs to and colour the robe.
- Cut out the figure and the robe and fit the robe using the fold-over tabs.

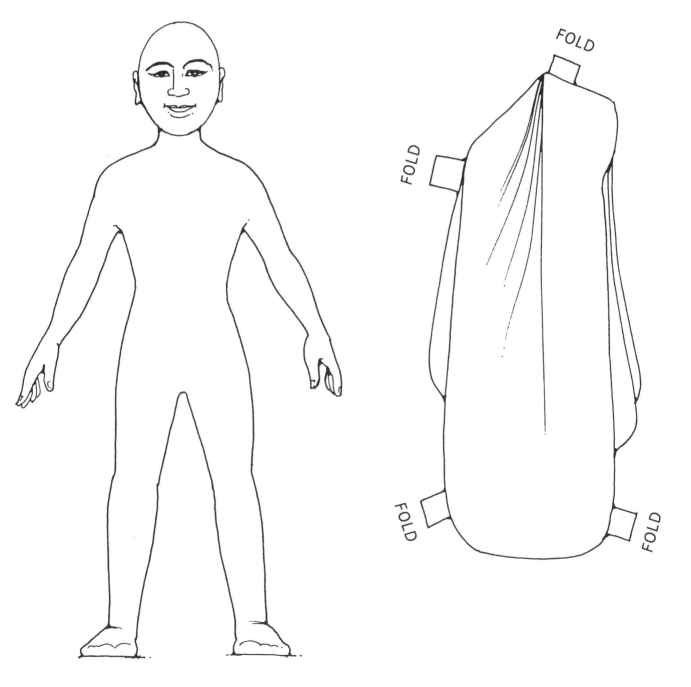

- Draw two gifts your monk is allowed to accept.
- Make new robes for the monk using coloured paper or fabric.

　　　IDEAS BANK – *Buddhism*

Glossary

Alms round Daily procession of monks or nuns to collect offerings of food from the lay people.

Ananda Cousin and devoted follower of the Buddha.

Bhikkhu Almsman, fully ordained Buddhist monk.

Bhikkhuni Almswoman, fully ordained Buddhist nun.

Bodhi Day Day commemorating the enlightenment of the Buddha.

Bodhi tree Tree under which the Buddha sat when he attained enlightenment.

Book of the Dead A book that discusses the concept of reincarnation.

Buddha 'Enlightened One'; name given to the man born as Siddattha Gotama.

Buddharupas (or rupas) Images of the Buddha.

Dalai Lama Excelled leader of Tibetan Buddhists.

Devadatta Cousin of the Buddha and his jealous rival.

Dhamma Right, virtue, truth or the teachings of the Buddha.

Dharmachakra The eight-spoked wheel of the law representing the Eightfold Path.

Dukkha The nature of existence, suffering, ill, unsatisfactoriness of life, nothing is certain.

Eightfold Path Code of belief governing a Buddhist's life and conduct.

Four Noble Truths The Buddha's teaching about suffering.

Gotama Family name of the Buddha.

Jataka Birth story and accounts of the early life of the Buddha.

Kamma Actions (ritual or moral) that affect one's fortune in this and future lives.

Kathina Day A day celebrating the end of the 'rains' retreat.

Kusinara Place in north India where the Buddha died, although this is under dispute.

Law of Impermanence The belief that everything changes, nothing stays the same.

Lotus position Position adopted for meditation.

Meditation Time spent quietly thinking, a time to empty the mind of desires.

Middle Way A moderate way of life advocated by the Buddha.

Nirvana 'Blowing out' (of the fires of greed, hatred and delusion) and the state of peace that follows.

Novice Trainee monk or nun.

Paritta Blessings recited by the monks.

Pitaka 'Basket' or collection of teachings or scriptures.

Reincarnation The belief that you are reborn into a new life after death.

Sangha 'Assembly'; often used for the order of bhikkhus and bhikkunis.

Stupa Burial mound or a mound containing relics. Smaller versions are made out of glass to cover images of the Buddha.

Sutta Pitaka Collection of scriptures containing the main teachings of the Buddha.

Theravada Way of the elders; the way of Buddhism prevalent in Thailand, Sri Lanka and so on.

Tibetan Buddhist Buddhists found in Tibet.

Vihara Dwelling place; monastery.

Wesak Name of festival and Sri Lankan word for the month of May. On the full moon of Wesak, the birth, enlightenment and death of the Buddha took place.

Zen A school of Mahayana Buddhism that developed in China and Japan.